BIG CATS, SMALL CATS

Contents

Dee Reid

Story illustrated by
Charlie Fowkes

Heinem

Before Reading

Find out about

- How lions are like cats

Tricky words

- hunting
- climbing
- water
- mane
- pride

Introduce these tricky words and help the reader when they come across them later!

Text starter

Lions are called big cats because lions do a lot of the same things that cats can do. Lions hunt and climb, and so do cats. But are lions really like cats?

Are Lions like Cats?

A lion is good at hunting.
Is a cat good at hunting?

A lion is good at climbing.

Is a cat good at climbing?

A lion doesn't like going in water.

Does a cat like going in water?

A lion has a mane.

Does a cat have a mane?

A lion lives in a pride.

Does a cat live in a pride?

A pride is a group of lions that live together.

A lion **ROARS**.

Does a cat roar?

A lion is big and strong.

Is a cat big and strong?

So are lions just like cats?

Do kittens like to play too?

Quiz

Text Detective

- Does a cat have a mane?
- Would you like a lion as a pet?

Word Detective

- **Phonic Focus:** Initial letter sounds
  Page 7: Find two words that start with 'l'.
- Page 9: Find the word 'big' twice.
- Page 9: Find a word that rhymes with 'long'.

Super Speller

Read these words:

at   like   has

Now try to spell them!

HA! HA! HA!

Q What do cats eat for breakfast?

A Mice Krispies!

11

In this story

 Mr Cross

 The children

 Leo the lion

Tricky words

- wake
- sleep
- children
- woke
- away
- roar

Introduce these tricky words and help the reader when they come across them later!

Story starter

Mr Cross was a teacher. One day, he took the children to the zoo. They went to see Leo the lion. "Leo is boring," said the children. "He's always asleep." "I'll wake him up," said Mr Cross.

Lazy Leo

"Wake up Leo," said Mr Cross.
"You can't sleep all day."

Leo didn't wake up.

"Wake up, Leo,"
said the children.
"Get up now."

Leo the lion woke up.

"Go away!" said Leo.

"You can't sleep all day,"
said Mr Cross.
"Be a good lion and get up."

"OK," said Leo.
"I will be a good lion."

How will Leo
be a good lion?

"Good lions roar!" said Leo.

And Leo roared and roared and roared.

"Stop!" said Mr Cross.

"Stop!" said the children.

"Can I sleep now?" said Leo.

"Yes you can," said Mr Cross.

"You can sleep all day," said the children.

Quiz

Text Detective

- Why did the children think Leo was boring?
- Do you think Leo is a good lion?

Word Detective

- **Phonic Focus:** Initial letter sounds
  Page 17: Find two words that start with 'g'.
- Page 21: Find the word 'said' twice.
- Page 21: Find a word that rhymes with 'hop'.

Super Speller

Read these words:

up   get   will

Now try to spell them!

HA! HA! HA!

Q What do you call an angry lion?

A Don't call it anything. Just run away!